Southend Road, Woodford Green, Essex IG8 8HN England
Music Arranged by Roger Day
Music Transcribed by Musicprint Limited
Photos on pages 4 and 5 by Peter Mac
Printed by Panda Press · Haverhill · Suffolk CB9 8PR
215-2-827

TAKE THAT - BIOGRAPHY

In the space of just one year, TAKE THAT have gone from being five ordinary Manchester lads to being the most popular teen idols in the country at the moment, their faces adorning bedroom walls up and down the country, causing scenes of mass hysteria wherever they appear. With a couple of Top Ten hit singles and a Top Five album already under their belts, TAKE THAT have established themselves as one of the pop successes of the year and with the success of their current single "A Million Love Songs" and their forthcoming national tour TAKE THAT mania looks set to continue!

TAKE THAT are - GARY BARLOW (21),HOWARD DONALD (22),JASON ORANGE (22), MARK OWEN (18) and ROBBIE WILLIAMS (18).

The TAKE THAT story began when Gary and Mark, who were in a group called "The Cutest Rush" joined forces with Howard and Jason's break dancing crew "Street Beat". With the addition of Robbie, TAKE THAT were complete. Having been turned down by a number of record companies, TAKE THAT decided to release their first single "Do What U Like" on their own label. Whilst failing to set the charts alight, "Do What U Like" won alot of media attention for the band, which in turn led to RCA Records signing a major album deal with TAKE THAT in September 1991.

"Promises", released in November 1991 was the band's first single for RCA. It entered the UK Top Forty in it's first week, debuting at number 38, a remarkable achievement for a new band at the most competitive time of the year chart wise. TAKE THAT's second single "Once You've Tasted Love", released in January '92, helped to maintain the band's evergrowing fan base and coincided with the band embarking on a major club tour - "The Safe Sex Tour" - organised in conjunction with the Family Association to increase awareness of safe sex amongst young people. However, it was the release of "It Only Takes A Minute" in May 1992 that cemented TAKE THAT's popularity. The band appeared at the Children's Royal Variety Performance and the single peaked at number 7 in the charts.

TAKE THAT's next single release "I Found Heaven", released in August, saw Robbie making his debut on lead vocals. Like it's predecessor, "I Found Heaven" zoomed straight into the Top Twenty! August '92 also saw the release of the boy's debut album "Take That And Party", which entered the charts at number 5 and went silver within one week. "Take That And Party" features all of the band's singles and also illustrates Gary's songwriting prowess, with 10 of it's 13 tracks his.compositions. To coincide with the release of the album TAKE THAT embarked on a series of signing sessions in record shops around the country, but after attracting an average of 3.000 fans per date, the tour ended up having to be cancelled in the interest of public safety. Indeed the chaos surrounding Take That has been such that TAKE THAT can rarely make an appearance without being mobbed by oneof the many "Take Thatters" and their ever-growing fan club now has over 20,000 members. TAKE THAT's wide appeal has also led to them getting substantial media coverage, with the band appearing on dozen's of tv programmes and magazine covers.

TAKE THAT's current single release "The Love Songs E.P." features one of the most popular songs from the album "A Million Love Songs" plus three other love songs all written and produced by Gary - "Still Can't Get Over You", "How Can It Be" and "Don't Take Your Love", with Mark sharing lead vocals with Gary on "How Can It Be". "A Million Love Songs" has already been tipped as a potential Number One by many, revealing a more sensuous romantic side to Take That, to those who only know them for their uptempo singles. The boys look set to win over more hearts when they embark on their first full nationwide tour in November.

TAKE THAT are:

GARY BARLOW (birthday January 20th, 1971)

Gary is the most musical member of the band, writing and co-producing many of the group's songs, he sings lead vocals on most of the tracks and has a small studio at home which he uses to write in. He loves good food (especially chinese food and chocolate!), going to the cinema and his two spaniel dogs Pete and Oliver.

HOWARD DONALD (birthday April 27th 1970)

On first impression, Howard appears to be the quietest member of the group, but anyone who get to know him, knows that he also possesses a very dry and rather wicked sense of humour! Howard is also acknowledged as "the body" of the band, as well as one of the best dancers, and has recently been approached by other bands to help them with their choreography. Howard loves collecting records and has a huge collection of 12"'s with secret hopes of being a DJ! He also plays the trumpet and the piano.

JASON ORANGE (birthday July 10th, 1970)

Jason is the most sensitive member of the group - taking an interest in environmental issues and trying hard to be vegetarian. Like Howard, he is known for his nifty footwork on the dancefloor, a skill he developed during the years he spent out dancing in clubs. He has a twin brother Justin, and shares a flat with another one of his many brothers. He also loves clothes and has a keen interest in fashion.

MARK OWEN (birthday January 27th 1974)

As the smallest member of Take That, Mark is often referred to as "the cute one", especially as he always has a smile on his face and a good word to say about everyone! He's a keen footballer and has won loads of trophies, and still enjoys working out and keeping fit. He's also both the worrier and organiser in the band, always making sure the other members are on time and feeling o.k. Mark recently won a Smash Hits poll as the most kissable male in the world, getting twice as many votes as the person who came second (who incidentally was Robbie!)

ROBBIE WILLIAMS (birthday February, 1974)

In spite of being the youngest member of the Take That posse, Robbie is also the loudest and is the joker of the band - always messing around, telling jokes, and generally annoying the others (but only in a nice way of course!). He's a keen supporter of Port Vale Football Club and still spends as much time on the terraces as he can. His latest hobby is rollerblading around the park and he's also a huge Vic Reeves fan. Robbie's vocal talents have also come to the fore recently, and he's featured on lead vocals on the single "I Found Heaven" and on the track "Could It Be Magic".

I Found Heaven

Words and Music by
IAN LEVINE/BILLY GRIFFIN

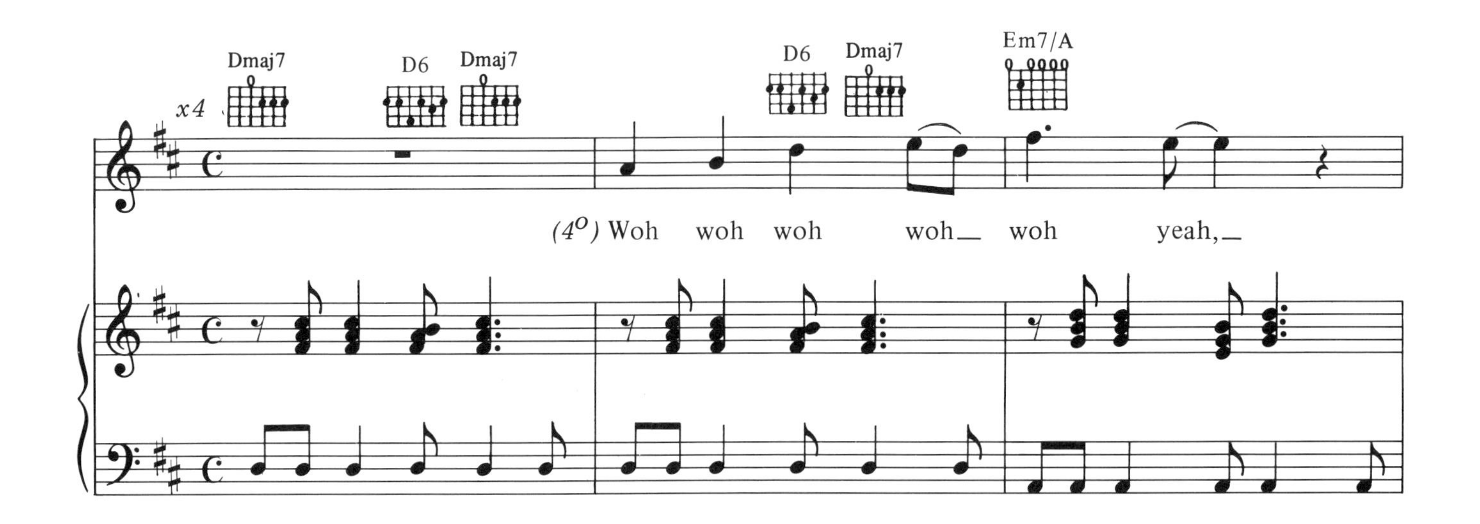

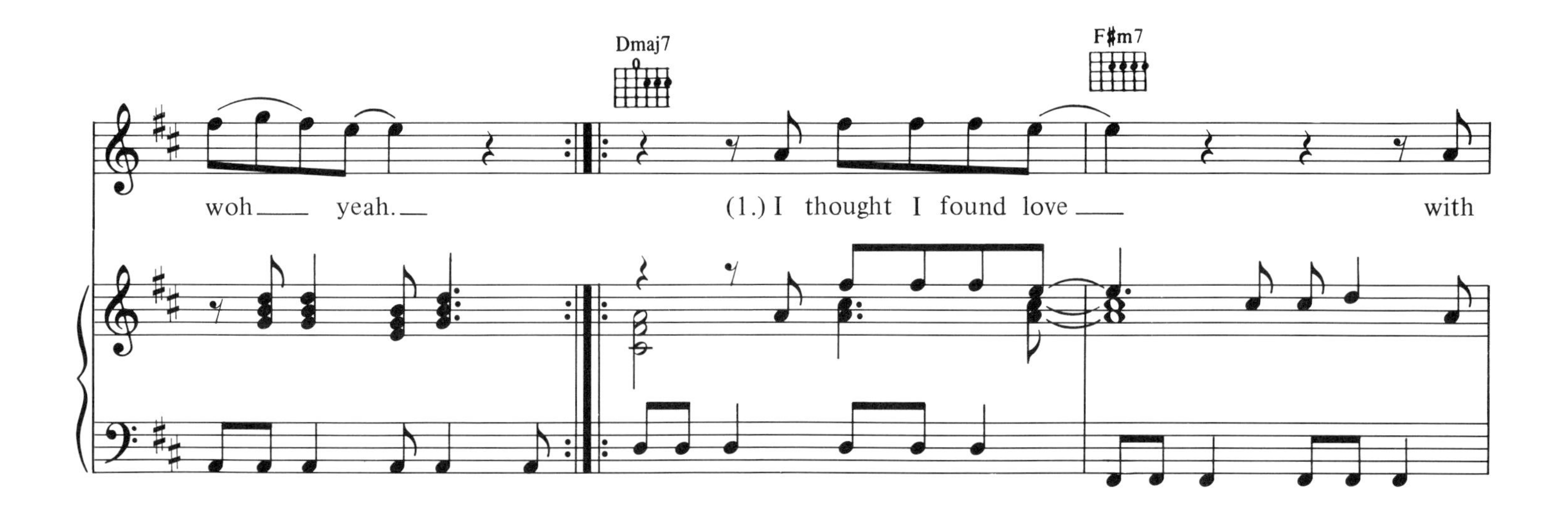

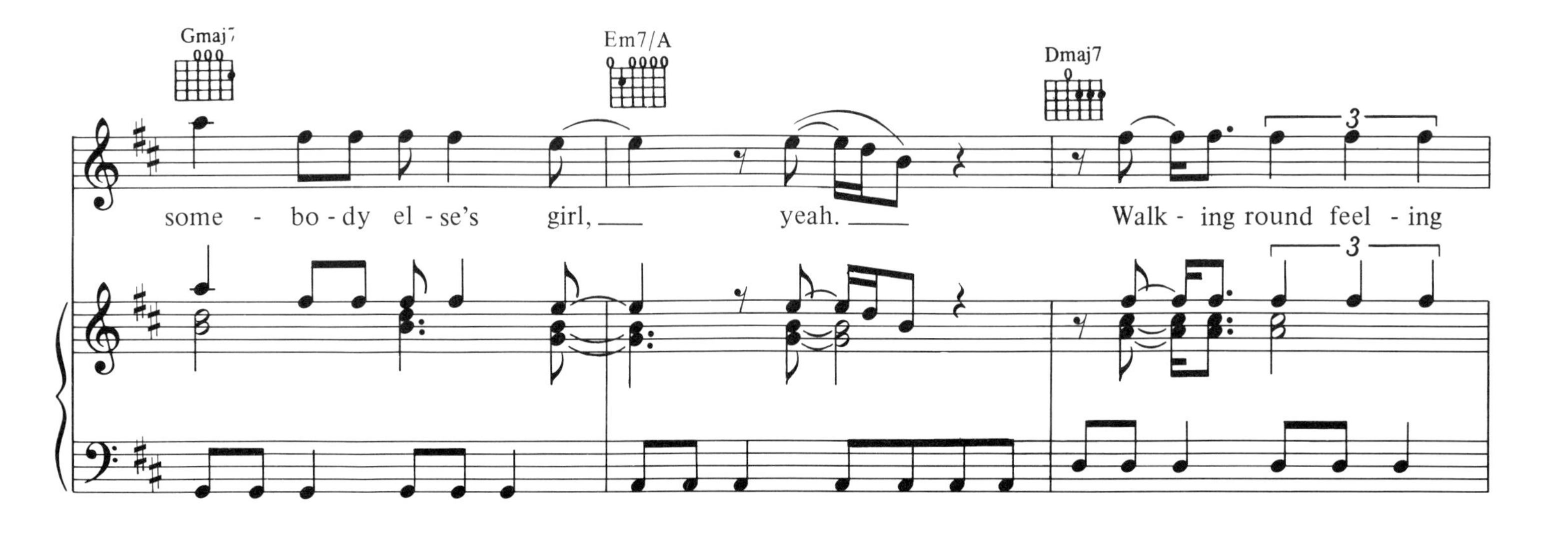

F♯m7
Gmaj7
Em7/A
so brok - en heart - ed lost in a dif - fe - rent world.
Em7
F♯m7
Gmaj7
Then you came in my life, brought me back to re -
F♯m7
Em7
F♯m7
al - i - ty so nice. Now I don't need a fan - ta - sy,
Gmaj7
Em7/A
Dmaj7
D6
you're the on - ly one I need. I found hea - ven, sweet

Dmaj7
Em7/A
hea - ven ba - by, on the wings of love. I found
Dmaj7
D6
Dmaj7
Em7/A
hea - ven, sweet hea - ven ba - by, on the wings of love.
Gmaj7
I will ne - ver, no I'll
D/A
Em7
ne - ver, I will ne - ver lose my way a - gain oh

Em7/A
Dmaj7
— yeah. ___
Em7/A
B♭maj7
Oh, I see
Fmaj7
hea-ven in your eyes for me. ___
Oh ba - by,
B♭maj7
Em7/A
now ___ I will give my lov-ing faith - ful-ly, ___ oh ___

VERSE 2:
I thought you'd soon be my girl
But my imagination was running wild;
I wouldn't listen to a single soul
Deep in a sense of denial
But then you rescued me baby,
Opened my eyes and made me see
What real love can be,
You're the angel that I need.

Once You've Tasted Love

Words and Music by
GARY BARLOW

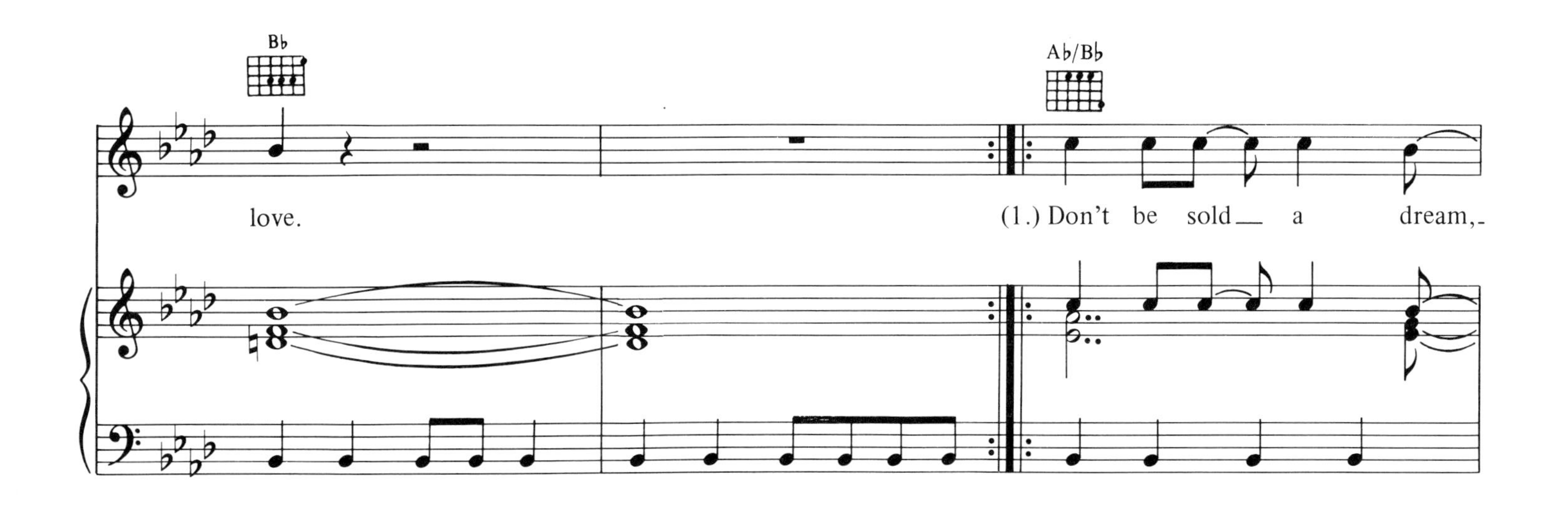

E♭/B♭
A♭/B♭
E♭/B♭
Re - mem-ber how the past has been,
A♭/B♭
E♭/B♭
B♭
don't be led to be - lieve this one's for you.
A♭/B♭
E♭/B♭
A♭/B♭
Cal - cu - late your needs I see there's room to plant your seeds,
E♭/B♭
A♭/B♭
E♭/B♭
don't de - cide till you see how the oth - ers have grown.

Bb
CHORUS
Db
Ab/C
Once you've tast - ed love it is just the be - gin -
Bbm
Fm
Db
ning of a new world. Once you've tast - ed love
Ab/C
Ebm
Fm
there's no way you can give in, oh no, once you've tast - ed
Bb
1.
2.
love. Once you've tast-ed

Bbm
Eb
Bbm
Eb
love,
once you've tast-ed
love,
once you've tast-ed
Bbm
Eb
Bb
F
love,
once you've tast-ed
love.
Db
Ab/C
Bbm
(1.) Once you've tast - ed
love it is just the be - gin - ning
of a new
(2.) can't con - trol your
mind and your head is still spin - ning
oh yeah,
Fm
Db
Ab/C
world.
Once you've tast - ed
love there's no way you can give
Once you've tast - ed
love it is just the be - gin -

1.
2.
Ebm
Fm
Bbmaj7
in, oh no. You - ing, once you've tast - ed love.
Bbm
Eb
You've tast - ed love, you know, it's good, come taste my love, you know you should.
RAP:
Come into my world as the badness disappears, take my hand, don't be afraid

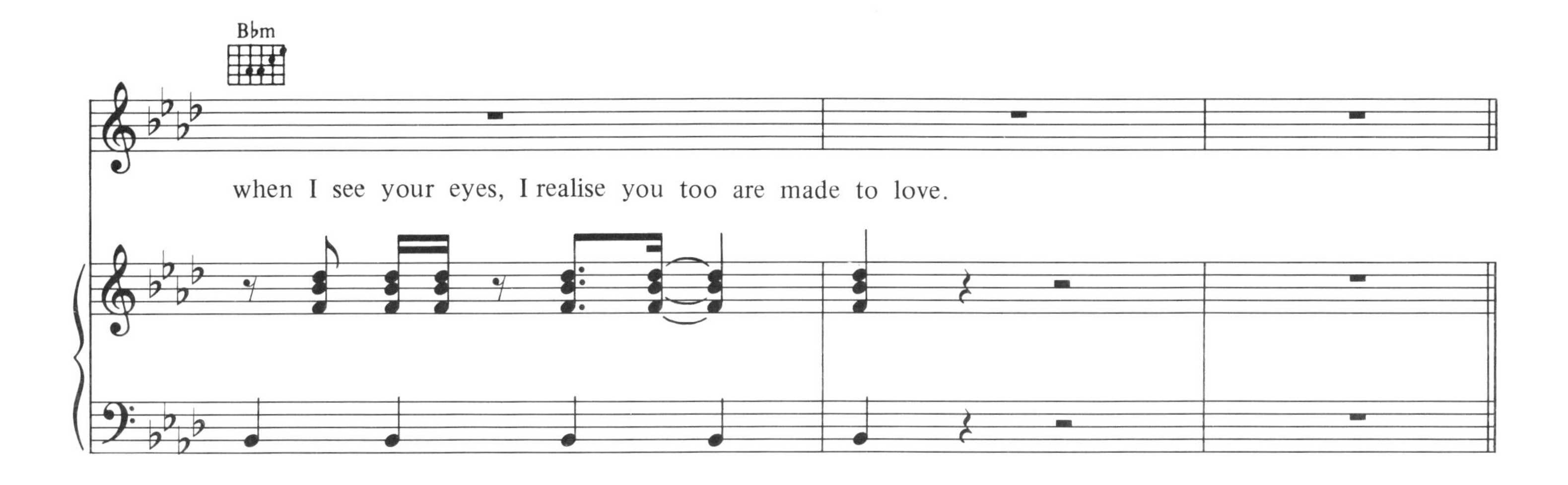

VERSE 2:
Still too early to know,
Give them time and they will grow;
Don't believe that the first one's the one for you.
Most will grow to be tall,
Others will break and fall;
Keep your eye on the strongest head of them all.

CHORUS 2:
Once you've tasted love
It is just the beginning of a new world.
Once you've tasted love
It is just the beginning, your head is spinning,
Once you've tasted love.

It Only Takes A Minute

Words and Music by
DENNIS LAMBERT/BRIAN POTTER

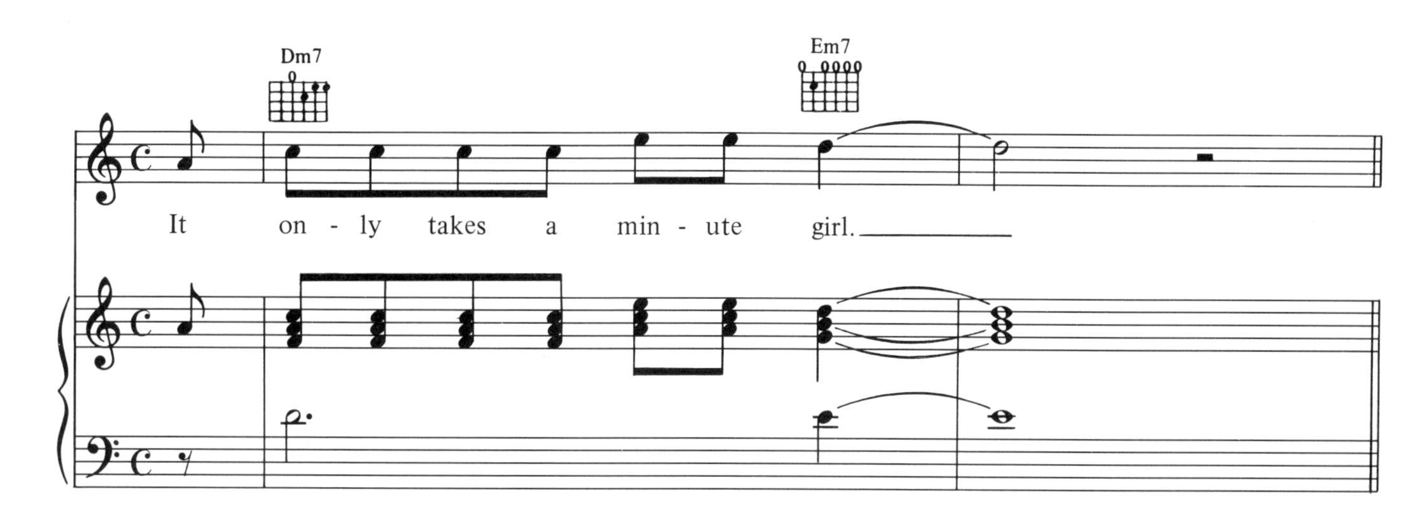

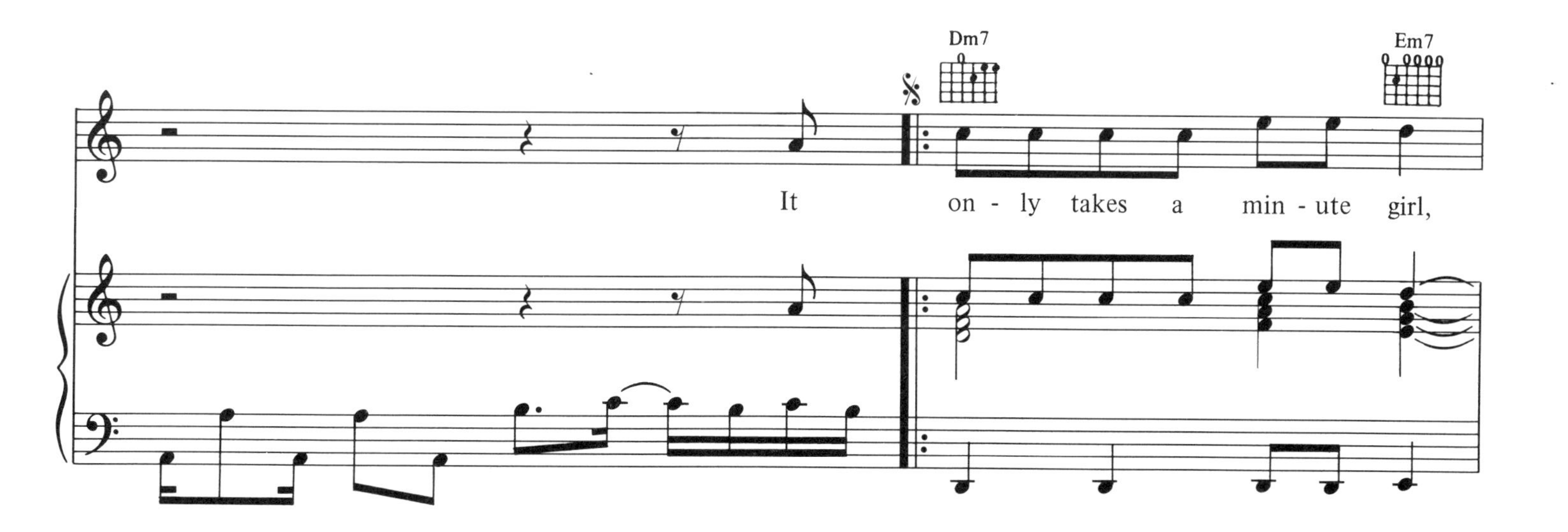

Dm7
/G
to fall in love, to fall in love. It
Dm7
Em7
Dm7
To Coda
only takes a minute girl to fall in love, to fall
/G
Am
in love.

Am
E+
(1.) What's an ho - ur of the day,
we throw at least one a - way.
E
Dm7
And walk the streets for half a year
E+
E
Am
trying to find a new ca - reer.
If you get a flu at - tack
E+
E
for thir - ty days you're on your back,

Dm7
do - in' not a sin - gle dance
ba - by give me half a chance.
E+
E
3º – D.S.
CODA
It
/G
in love.
It
Dm7
Em7
Dm7
on - ly takes a min - ute girl,
to fall in love,
to
/G
Dm7
Em7
fall in love.
It on - ly takes a min - ute girl
to

VERSE 2:
In the unemployment lines
You can spend your life reading signs,
Waiting for your interview
They can shoot the whole day for you.
Now winter's gonna turn to spring
And you haven't accomplished a thing,
So baby can you make me just a little time
'Cause you never know what's on my mind.

A Million Love Songs

Words and Music by
GARY BARLOW

Ab
Gb
Db
mil - lion words just try - ing to make the love song of the year.
Db
Gb/Db
Close your eyes but don't for - get what you have heard, a
Ab
Gb
Db
man who's trying to say three words, words that make me scared. A mil - lion
Ebm7
Ab7
Db
Ab/C
love songs la - ter here I am try- ing to tell you that I

B♭7
E♭m7
A♭
care. A mil - lion love songs la - ter and here I am,
D♭
A♭/C
B♭7
E♭m7
here I am, a mil - lion love songs la - ter
/A♭
1.
D♭
A♭/C
B♭7
here I am.
E♭m7
A♭
G♭/A♭
A♭
2.
D♭

VERSE 2:
Looking to the future now, this is what I see,
A million chances pass me by, a million chances to hold you.
Take me back, take me back to where I used to be,
Hide away from all my truths, through the light I see.

CHORUS:
A million love songs later,
Here I am trying to tell you that I care.
A million love songs later,
And here I am, just for you girl;
A million love songs later,
Here I am.

Satisfied

Words and Music by
GARY BARLOW

C Gm7 F B♭ C F
you've been treat - ing me. I pro - mised you no - thing and gave you much more
B♭ F C Gm F B♭
To Coda
CHORUS
making love is all you want - ed me for. 'Cause you're ne - ver sa -
C Gm B♭ F B♭ C Gm B♭ F B♭
tis - fied, you're ne - ver sa - tis - fied. If you o - pen up
C Gm B♭ F B♭ C Gm B♭
your mind you'll see that you could be sa - tis - fied with me.

1.
2.
F
C
G
Bb
(2.) Ba - by you cri -
(See lyric at bottom)
You can be
if you wan - na be,
you can be
if you wan - na be,
you can be
if you wan - na be,
you can be
N.C.
if you wan - na be.
(3.) I of - ten won -
(See lyric at bottom)
D.%. al Coda
CODA
Gm
When will you be sa -

F Bb C Bb 1. F Bb
tis - fied? When will you be sa - tis - fied?
2.
C Gm Bb
tis - fied? You're ne-ver sa - tis - fied,
tis - fied,
F Bb C Gm Bb F Bb
you're ne-ver sa - tis-fied. If you e-ver change
you're ne-ver sa - tis-fied. If you o-pen up
C Gm Bb F Bb 1. C Gm Bb
your mind you'll see that you could be sa - tis-fied with me.
your mind you'll see that you could be sa -

2.
F
B♭
N.C.
'Cause you're ne-ver sa- - is - fied.
C
Gm
B♭
F
B♭
N.C.
x4
When will you __ be sa - tis - fied? __
RAP 1:
C
B♭/C
C
B♭/C
I'm watching you to see, I don't like the way you've been treating me;
C
B♭/C
C
B♭/C
C
I promised you nothing and gave you much more making love is all you wanted me for. Baby, you criticise my every move,

VERSE 2:
Baby you criticise my every move,
Look, can't you see I got nothing to prove?
I've had enough, it's a matter of time,
Maybe we'll make it somewhere down the line.

CHORUS:
You're never satisfied,
You're never satisfied;
If you open up your mind you'll see
That you could be satisfied with me.

VERSE 3 (D.S.)
I often wonder what I see in you,
You don't do the things that I want you to do.
I open my eyes, I dream it's alright,
Maybe we'll make it together tonight.

I Can Make It

Words and Music by
GARY BARLOW

C
D
G
to be a - lone.
Not sure where I want to be,
so close to find-ing my dream.
Em
C
Bm7
Am7
We need to hold on to all the times we spoke of love,
Em
C
D
now I pray to God a - bove that some-day I can find the door I'm look-ing for.
G
C
D
Em
Am7
G/B
I can make it, I know I can, I can save this love for -

D
G
C
D
Em
e - ver.
I can make it, I know I can, we can
Am7
G/B
1. D
G
make this work to - ge - ther,
to - ge - ther.
2. D
C
D
G
Em
- ge - ther 'cause you know what this love means to me, you

C
D
Em
G/B
C
Bm7
know how it feels? When I can see it in your face that you're miss-ing me now, you
C
Bm7
C
A/C♯
feel I've let you down, you've got-ta hold on, you've got-ta reach out and be - lieve.
D
G
C
- er.)
D
Em
Am7
G/B
1.
D
We can make it to - geth -

VERSE 2:
It's not a lonely man's dream,
It's just that now there's been
A taste of love in my life
That I refuse to return
I've got so much to learn
How can I feel as though
I've reached the top of this steep hill
For a moment I was standing still,
Now I have the faith I've needed
To believe.

Do What You Like

Words and Music by
GARY BARLOW/RAY HEDGES

(Instr. on 𝄋.)
Cm
F
(1.) Su - gar sweet if on - ly they all knew
jam can't spread no more, you've took my bread;
e - ner - gy just
work no rest or play.
(Vocal in on D.𝄋.)
me, my - self I'd ra - ther be a - lone a - gain,
CHORUS
Now you can
C
G
do what you like
(do what you like)

C
G
C
no need to ask me, (do what you want). Do what you like
G
C
1.
G
no need to tell me (do what you want).
(do what you like)
2.
G
Em
F
Em
G
Em
F
Dm
G

VERSE 2:
Cherry pie,
You're not as cute as me;
Ice
Could never be as cold as you;
Recipe,
You stir me up inside;
Me, myself, I'd rather be alone again.

Promises

Words and Music by
GARY BARLOW/GRAHAM STACK

G
F6
C
D
E♭
there's got-ta be some-thing wrong.
What you tell-ing me that_ for
when you don't mean it?
What you tell-ing me that_ for
I don't be-lieve it. Your
pro-mi-ses_ have ne-ver been_
a-ny-thing_ you make_ them seem,_ so
what you gon-na pro-mise me this_
_ time?
You're tell-ing lies,_ so plain to see_ you're
trying to make a fool of me, so

VERSE 2:
Seems like I've been playing your game
And how you think you've won.
But when you count up what you've gained,
You're the lonely one.

Why Can't I Wake Up With You

Words and Music by
GARY BARLOW

Am7
Em7
o - pen mind
till the day
sets in.
1o only
C
Hear you call
me,
I'm so
G
will - ing to call
back.
C
Hear you
think - ing,
Em7
Am7
hope you hear
me think - ing too.

G
Cmaj7
Am7
Why can't I wake up with you
so you're there when I o - pen my eyes?
Ba - by why can't I wake up with you?
You're my life.
Cmaj9
1.
Em7
2.
(2.) Oh I

G
Cmaj7
Am7
G
Cmaj7
Am7
G
Cmaj7
Am7
Cmaj7
Em
So good to be near you,
Cmaj7
Em
Cmaj7
So dark when you walk from my side.
Ba - by why can't I wake
Em
Fmaj7
up with you? You're my life.
(whisper) You're my life.

a tempo
Am7
Em7
Am7
Em7
I hear you
C
Em
Am7
think - ing
hope you hear me think-ing too.
G
Cmaj7
Am7
G
Cmaj7
(1.) Why can't I wake up with you so you're there when I o - pen my eyes?
(2.) Why can't I wake up with you so you're there when I o - pen my eyes?

VERSE 2:
Oh, I feel alive, so I'll just begin
Yeah, to rest my mind before you ring me,
I hear you thinking, hope you hear me thinking too.

Never Want To Let You Go

Words and Music by
GARY BARLOW

Bbm
Eb
Fm
Eb
Count - ing curls in your hair, as you sleep so tight,
Bbm
Eb
Fm
Eb
I won-der if you'll e - ver know how you stim - u - late my life.
Gb/Ab
Dbmaj7
I don't know where I'm gon - na be go - ing babe, I'll ne-ver know
Cm7
F
till I go.

G♭/A♭
D♭maj7
The chan - ces are you'll be there too some day; we'll ne - ver know,
Cm7
F
let's hope,
B♭m
E♭
Fm
E♭
I ne - ver want to let you go,
B♭m
E♭
Fm
E♭
I ne - ver want to let you go, oh ba - by

Bbm
Eb
Fm
all I can do is hope,
'cause I ne-ver want to let you
go.
I can't stop
I can't think,
I can't stop,
Can't see, I can't see, no, can't think, I can't think, no;

Bbm
Fm
can't stop, there's no way out now.
I can't see,
Can't see, I can't see, no; can't think, I can't think, no,
I can't think, I can't stop.
there's no way out now.
Gb/Ab
Fm7
Em7
Ebm7
/Ab
I don't know whe - ther I'm try - ing to love you ba - by,

VERSE 2:
Dreaming soft in silence, been working hard all day,
Still the night goes dark I'm with you in every way.
I don't know where I'm gonna be going babe,
I'll never know till I go.
The chances are you'll be there too some day,
We'll never know, let's hope.

Give Good Feeling

Words and Music by
GARY BARLOW

F♯
G♯m
some-thing good is gon-na hap-pen.
I can't be-
G♯m
lieve in this world I see; I reach out to you, set me
free from these chains; I'm
E
hold-ing on,
F♯
try-ing hard
G♯m
just so you know I'm here
E
wait-ing
F♯sus4
for you
F♯
to
E
give good feel-ing to

F♯sus4
F♯
A
B
me, ba - by I know this feel - ing won't go.
E
F♯sus4
F♯
A
Makes you want to be free in a world where we fly, fly, fly.
B
D.𝄋. al Coda
To Coda ⊕
⊕ CODA
C♯m7
Come on and fly,
come on let's fly.

G♯m
1.
2.
G♯m
If you think I'm cra - zy for
lov - ing you ba - by, then I will show you the way that I feel.
E
F♯sus4
F♯
D♯m7

VERSE 2:
Don't let me go, I will be your prisoner;
Hold me down
And I will give you my reasons for loving you,
Needing you, can't do without ya.

If you think I'm crazy for loving you baby,
Then I must show you the way that I feel;
I'm holding on, trying hard
Just so you know I'm here waiting, so please

Take That And Party

Words and Music by
GARY BARLOW/RAY HEDGES

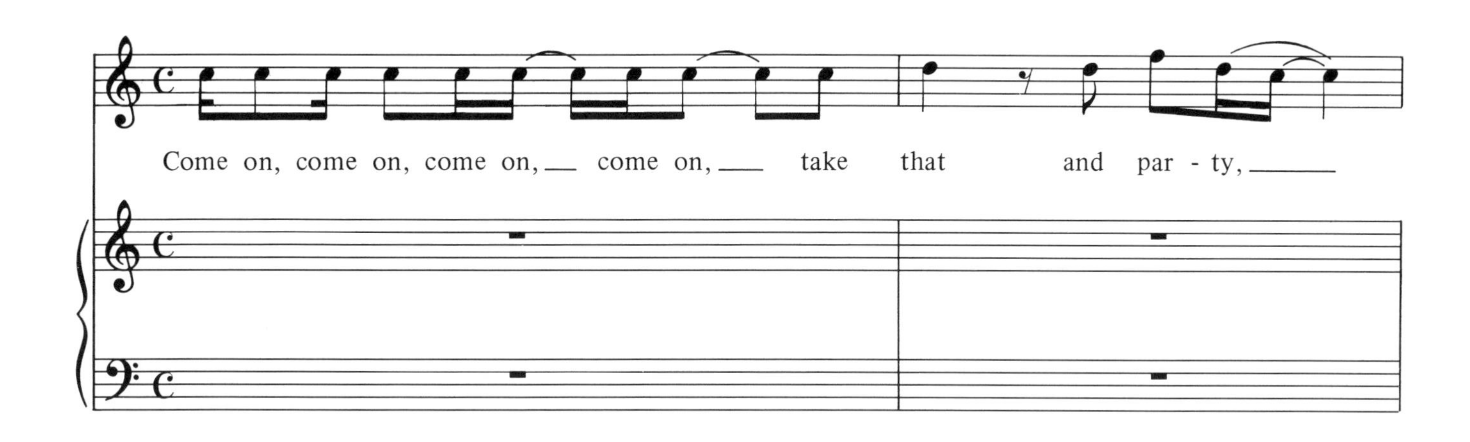

1º and 𝄋. only
To Coda ⊕
Dm7
(1.) Ev - 'ry part of you
G/D
makes me feel
Dm7
that I've got - ta touch you, you
G/D
know;
Dm7
if on - ly you knew what's in my
G/D
mind,
B♭/D
I can't be - lieve this
C/D
girl.
3

Dm7
Dm7
Oh oh come on, come on, come on, come on, take
Em7
F
(take that)
that and par - ty, come on, come on, come on, come on, take
G
Dm7
that. Come on, come on, come on, come, on, take
Em7
F
G
D.S. al Coda
(take that)
that and par-ty, come on, come on, come on, come on, take that.

CODA
Take that . . .
Come on, come on come on, come on, take
(take that)
that and par - ty,
come on, come on, come on, come on, take
that.
Dm7
Em7
Come on, come on, come on, come on, take
that and par - ty,

VERSE 2:
Don't catch the ball when I play real hard,
You'll never stop all my games.
If only you knew what's in my mind,
I can't believe this world.

Could It Be Magic

Words and Music by
BARRY MANILOW/ADRIENNE ANDERSON

Fm/A♭
B♭m
C
Fm
D♭
G♭
Oo wah oo wah.
C+
C7
Fm
Fsus4
F
(1.) Spi-rits move.
(2.) (See block lyric)

G
A♭maj7
Gm7
me ev - 'ry time I'm near you,
A♭maj7
Gm7
Csus4
C
whirl - ing like a cy - clone in my mind.
Gm/B♭
Fsus4
F
G
You're my life - line,
(𝄋. — see block lyric)
A♭maj7
Gm7
A♭maj7
an - gel of my life - time,
ans - wer to all ans -

CHORUS
Gm7
Csus4
C
C/Bb
Fm/Ab
C7/G
wers I can find.
Baby I want you; come,
Fm
Db/F
C/E
come,
come into my arms
Ebmaj7
Eb6
Dm7
Db-5
let me feel the wonder of all
C
C/Bb
Fm/Ab
C7/G
Fm
of you.
Could it be magic now,

Db/F
C/E
Ebmaj7
Eb6
now, now and hold on fast,
Dm7
Db-5
C
could this be the ma - gic at last.
Gm/Bb
F/A
Ab/Bb
Bb9
Ma - gic ah.
Dm
G/A
Doo wah doo doo wah

Dm9
wo doo wah doo
G/A
Em9
doo wah. There is ma-
Bm7
-gic in your eyes, doo doo
Em9
Am9
wah, doo doo wah.

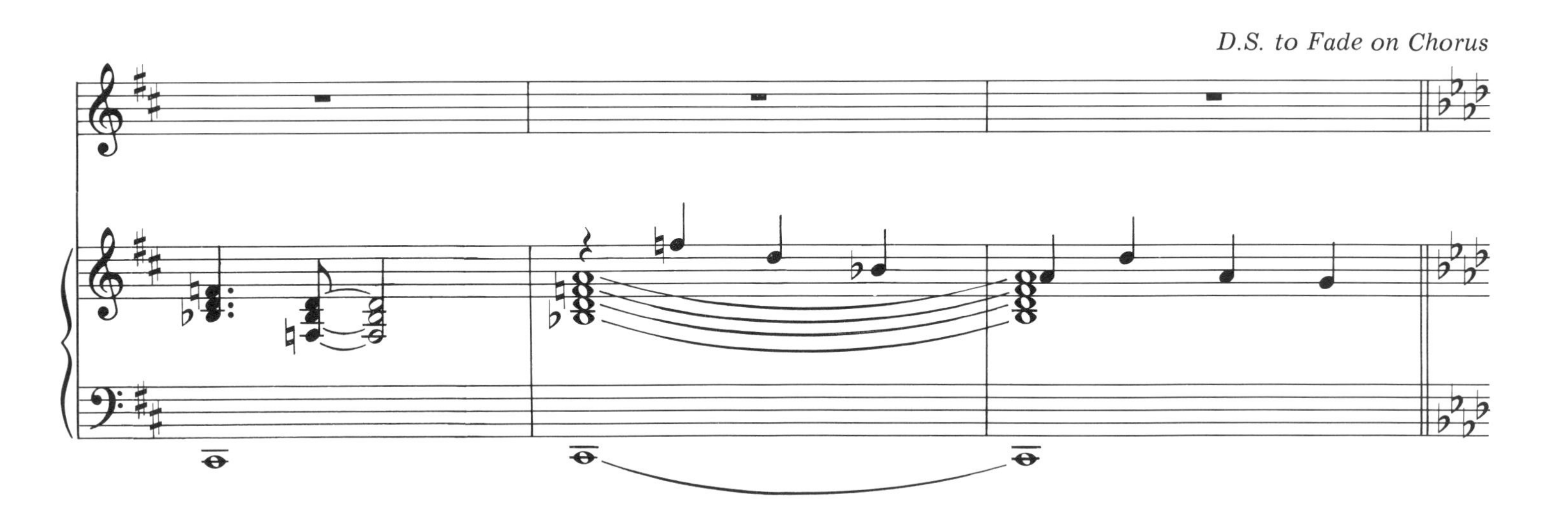

VERSE 2:
Baby take me high upon a hillside,
High up where the stallion meets the sun.
I could love you, build my world around you,
Never leave you till my life is done.

Printed in England
Panda Press · Haverhill · Suffolk • 8/94

It Only Takes A Minute

It only takes a minute girl.

Chorus
It only takes a minute girl
To fall in love, to fall in love.
It only takes a minute girl
To fall in love, to fall in love.

Verse 1
What's an hour of the day?
We throw at least one away.
And walk the streets for half a year
Trying to find a new career.
If you get a flu attack
For thirty days you're on your back
Doin' not a single dance,
Baby give me half a chance.

Chorus
It only takes a minute girl
To fall in love, to fall in love.
It only takes a minute girl
To fall in love, to fall in love.

Verse 2
In the unemployment lines
You can spend your life reading signs,
Waiting for your interview
They can shoot the whole day for you.
Now winter's gonna turn to spring
And you haven't accomplished a thing,
So baby can't you make me just a little time
'Cause you never know what's on my mind.

Chorus
It only takes a minute girl
To fall in love, to fall in love.
It only takes a minute girl
To fall in love, to fall in love.
repeat

Come on now, dance...

Chorus
It only takes a minute girl
To fall in love, to fall in love.
It only takes a minute girl
To fall in love, to fall in love.
repeat to fade

Once You've Tasted Love

Love,
Once you've tasted love.
Love,
Once you've tasted love.

Verse 1
Don't be sold a dream,
Remember how the past has been;
Don't be led to believe this one's for you.
Calculate your needs
I see there's room to plant your seeds;
Don't decide till you see how the others
have grown.

Chorus
Once you've tasted love
It is just the beginning of a new world.
Once you've tasted love
There's no way you can give in, oh no;
Once you've tasted love.

Verse 2
Still too early to know,
Give them time and they will grow;
Don't believe that the first one's the one
for you.
Most will grow to be tall,
Others will break and fall;
Keep your eye on the strongest head of
them all.

Chorus
Once you've tasted love
It is just the beginning of a new world.
Once you've tasted love
It is just the beginning, your head is
spinning,
Once you've tasted love.

Once you've tasted love...

Chorus
Once you've tasted love
It is just the beginning of a new world.
Once you've tasted love
There's no way you can give in, oh no.

You can't control your mind
And your head is still spinning, oh yeah.
Once you've tasted love
It is just the beginning.

Once you've tasted love.
You've tasted love, you know it's good.
Come taste my love, you know you should.

Rap
Come into my world as the badness disappears,
Take my hand, don't be afraid, I will work on all your fears.
They say so much and they give you only a glove,
When I see your eyes I realise you too are made to love.

You've tasted love, you know it's good,
Come taste my love, you know you should.

I Found Heaven

Verse 1
I thought I found love
With somebody else's girl, yeah;
Walking round feeling so brokenhearted,
Lost in a different world.
Then you came in my life,
Brought me back to reality so nice.
Now I don't need a fantasy,
You're the only one I need.

Chorus
I found heaven, sweet heaven, baby
On the wings of love.
I found heaven, sweet heaven, baby
On the wings of love.
I will never, no I'll never,
I will never lose my way again, oh yeah.

Verse 2
I thought you'd soon be my girl
But my imagination was running wild;
I wouldn't listen to a single soul
Deep in a sense of denial.
But then you rescued me baby,
Opened my eyes and really seen me
What real love can be,
You're the angel that I need.

Chorus
I found heaven, sweet heaven, baby
On the wings of love.
I found heaven, sweet heaven, baby
On the wings of love.
I will never, no I'll never,
I will never lose my way again, oh sweet baby.

Middle
Oh, I see heaven in your eyes for me
Oh baby;
Now I will give my loving faithfully,
Oh sweet baby, be my angel

Chorus
I found heaven, sweet heaven, baby
On the wings of love.
repeat ad lib. to fade

Satisfied

Verse 1
Baby I'm watching you to see,
I don't like the way you've been treating me.
I promised you nothing and gave you much more,
Making love is all you wanted me for.

Chorus
'Cause you're never satisfied,
You're never satisfied;
If you open up your mind you'll see
That you could be satisfied with me.

Verse 2
Baby you criticise my every move,
Look, can't you see I got nothing to prove?
I've had enough, it's a matter of time,
Maybe we'll make it somewhere down the line.

Chorus
You're never satisfied,
You're never satisfied;
If you open up your mind you'll see
That you could be satisfied with me.

You can be if you wanna be...

Verse 3
I often wonder what I see in you,
You don't do the things that I want you to do.
I open my eyes, and dream it's alright,
Maybe we'll make it together tonight.

When will you be satisfied?...

Chorus
You're never satisfied,
You're never satisfied;
If you open up your mind you'll see
That you could be satisfied with me.

'Cause you're never satisfied,
You're never satisfied;
If you open up your mind you'll see
That you could be satisfied.

When will you be satisfied?...

Rap 1
I'm watching you to see, I don't like the way you treat me;
I promise you not to give you much more, making love so you want anymore.
Baby, you criticise my every move, can't you see I've got nothing to prove?
I open my eyes and I dream it's alright, maybe we can make it again.

Be satisfied...
ad lib.

Rap 2
I said baby, I got nothing to prove, you never keep me satisfied, you see,
You never keep me satisfied, you see; you never keep me satisfied, you see.
I said baby, you never keep me, you never keep me, you never keep me satisfied,
Open up your eyes and see.
ad lib. to fade

A Million Love Songs

Verse 1
Put your head against my life, what do you hear?
A million words just trying to make the love song of the year.
Close your eyes, but don't forget what you have heard,
A man who's trying to say three words, words that make me scared.

Chorus
A million love songs later,
And here I am trying to tell you that I care
A million love songs later,
And here I am, here I am;
A million love songs later,
And here I am.

Verse 2
Looking to the future now, this is what I see,
A million chances pass me by, a million chances to hold you.
Take me back, take me back to where I used to be,
And hide away from all my truths, through the light I see.

Chorus
A million love songs later,
And here I am trying to tell you that I care.
A million love songs later,
And here I am, just for you girl;
A million love songs later,
And here I am.

Feel for you baby,
Feel for you baby.
A million love songs later,
And here I...here I am.

I Can Make It

Verse 1
I'm tired of closing my eyes
To picture you in my mind,
It feels so cold to be alone.
Not sure where I want to be,
So close to finding my dream.
We need to hold on
To all the times we spoke of love;
Now I pray to God above
That some day I can find the door
I'm looking for.

Chorus
I can make it, I know I can,
I can save this love for ever.
I can make it, I know I can,
We can make this work together, together.

Verse 2
It's not a lonely man's dream,
It's just that now there's been
A taste of love in my life
That I refuse to return.
I've got so much to learn,
How can I feel as though
I've reached the top of this steep hill?
For a moment I was standing still,
Now I have the faith I've needed
To believe.

Chorus
I can make it, I know I can,
I can save this love for ever.
I can make it, I know I can,
I can make this work together.

Middle
'Cause you know what this love means to me
You know how it feels when I can see it in your face,
That you're missing me now, you feel I've let you down
You've gotta hold on, you've gotta reach out and believe.

We can make it together
'Cause I believe we can make love forever.

I can make this world a better place
For me and you.
repeat to fade

Do What You Like

Verse 1
Sugar sweet,
If only they all knew;
Jam,
Can't spread no more, you've took my
  bread;
Energy,
Just work, no rest or play;
Me, myself, I'd rather be alone again.

Chorus
So you can do what you like,
(Do what you like)
No need to ask me,
(Do what you want)
Do what you like,
(Do what you like)
No need to tell me.
(Do what you want)

Verse 2
Cherry pie,
You're not as cute as me;
Ice
Could never be as cold as you;
Recipe,
You stir me up inside;
Me, myself, I'd rather be alone again.

Chorus
So you can do what you like,
(Do what you like)
No need to ask me,
(Do what you want)
Do what you like,
(Do what you like)
No need to tell me.
(Do what you want)

Additional chorus
Do what you like,
(Do what you like)
No need to ask me,
(Do what you want)
Do what you like,
No need to tell me.

Do what you like,
  (I know)
Do what you want,
  (To me)
Do what you like,
Do what you want.

Verse 3 *(D.𝄋.)*
instrumental, 6 bars
Me, myself, I'd rather be alone again.

Chorus
Now you can do what you like,
(Do what you like)
No need to ask me,
(Do what you want)
Do what you like,
(Do what you like)
No need to tell me.
(Do what you want)
repeat to fade

Why Can't I Wake Up With You

Verse 1
Oh, I can't decide if I should read or think,
I'll keep an open mind till the day sets in.
Hear you call me; I'm so willing to call back.
Hear you thinking, hope you hear me thinking too.

Chorus
Why can't I wake up with you
So you're there when I open my eyes?
Baby why can't I wake up with you?
You're my life.

Verse 2
Oh, I feel alive, so I'll just begin
Yeah, to rest my mind before you ring me.
I hear you thinking, hope you hear me thinking too.

Chorus
Why can't I wake up with you
So you're there when I open my eyes?
Baby why can't I wake up with you?
You're my life.

So good to be near you,
So dark when you walk from my side.
Baby why can't I wake up with you?
You're my life.
(whisper) You're my life.

Verse 3
instrumental, 8 bars
I hear you thinking, hope you hear me thinking too.

Chorus
Why can't I wake up with you
So you're there when I open my eyes?
Baby why can't I wake up with you?
You're my life.

Why don't we dream this at night,
So you're there when the dark turns to light?
Baby I know this is right,
You're my life.

Promises

Verse 1
Standing back I can't believe
How you've led me on.
And judging by the things you say
There's gotta be something wrong.

What you telling me that for
When you don't mean it?
What you telling me that for?
I don't believe it.

Chorus
Your promises have never been
Anything you made them seem,
So what you gonna promise me this time?
You're telling lies, so plain to see,
You're trying to make a fool of me,
So what you gonna promise me this time?
I wanna know.

Verse 2
Seems like I've been playing your game
And how you think you've won.
But when you count up what you've gained,
You're the lonely one.

What you telling me that for
When you don't mean it?
What you telling me that for?
I don't believe it.

Chorus
Your promises have never been
Anything you made them seem,
So what you gonna promise me this time?
You're telling lies, so plain to see,
You're trying to make a fool of me,
So what you gonna promise me this time? *(repeat chorus)*

...I wanna know.

Verse 3
instrumental

What you telling me that for
When you don't mean it?
What you telling me that for?
I don't believe it.

Chorus
Your promises have never been
Anything you made them seem,
So what you gonna promise me this time?
You're telling lies, so plain to see,
You're trying to make a fool of me,
So what you gonna promise me this time?
repeat ad lib. to fade

Never Want To Let You Go

Verse 1
Lying here beside you, in a cloud of warmth,
I've been awake all night but move, though I know I should.
Counting curls in your hair, as you sleep so tight
I Wonder if you'll ever know how you stimulate my life.
I don't know where I'm gonna be going babe,
I'll never know till I go.
The chances are you'll be there too some day,
We'll never know, let's hope..

Chorus
I never want to let you go,
I never want to let you go,
Oh baby, all I can do is hope
'Cause I never want to let you go.

Verse 2
Dreaming soft in silence, been working hard all day,
Still the night grows darker, I'm with you now in every way.
I don't know where I'm gonna be going babe,
I'll never know till I go.
The chances are you'll be there too some day,
We'll never know, let's hope.

Chorus
I never want to let you go,
I never want to let you go,
Oh baby, all I can do is hope
'Cause I never want to let you go.

Never wanna let you go...

I can't see,
(Can't see, I can't see, no)
I can't think,
(Can't think, I can't think, no)
I can't stop.
(Can't stop, there's no way out now)
I can't see,
(Can't see, I can't see, no)
I can't think,
(Can't think, I can't think, no)
I can't stop.
(Can't stop, there's no way out now)

I don't know whether I'm trying to love you baby,
Been around for long enough to know.
The chances are you'll be there too some day,
We'll never know, let's hope.

Chorus
I never want to let you go,
I never want to let you go,
Oh baby, all I can do is hope
'Cause I never want to let you go.
ad lib. repeats to fade

Take That And Party

Verse 1
Every part of you makes me feel
That I've gotta touch you, you know;
If only you knew what's in my mind,
I can't believe this girl.

Chorus
Come on, come on, come on, come on,
Take that (take that) and party.
Come on, come on, come on, come on,
Take that.
Come on, come on, come on, come on,
Take that (take that) and party.
Come on, come on, come on, come on,
Take that.

Verse 2
Don't catch the ball when I play real hard,
You'll never stop all my games.
If only you knew what's in my mind,
I can't believe this world.

Chorus
Come on, come on, come on, come on,
Take that (take that) and party.
Come on, come on, come on, come on,
Take that.
Come on, come on, come on, come on,
Take that (take that) and party.
Come on, come on, come on, come on,
Take that.

Take that...

Chorus
Come on, come on, come on, come on,
Take that (take that) and party.
Come on, come on, come on, come on,
Take that.
Come on, come on, come on, come on,
Take that (take that) and party.
Come on, come on, come on, come on,
Take that.
repeat ad lib.

Give Good Feeling

Verse 1
You've got to hold me and control my dreams;
I want you to fulfil my needs;
I feel it babe,
Something good is gonna happen.
I can't believe in this world I see;
I reach out to you, set me free from these chains;
I'm holding on, trying hard
Just so you know I'm here waiting for you to

Chorus
Give good feeling to me,
Baby I know this feeling won't go.
Makes you want to be free
In a world where we fly, fly, fly.

Verse 2
Don't let me go, I will be your prisoner;
Hold me down
And I will give you my reasons for loving you,
Needing you, can't do without ya.
If you think I'm crazy for loving you baby,
Then I will show you the way that I feel;
I'm holding on, trying hard
Just so you know I'm here waiting, so please

Chorus
Give good feeling to me,
Baby I know this feeling won't go.
Makes you want to be free
In a world where we fly, fly, fly.
(repeat)

Come on and fly,
Come on let's fly...

If you think I'm crazy for loving you baby,
Then I will show you the way that I feel;
Give good feeling to me.

Chorus
Give good feeling to me,
Baby I know this feeling won't go.
Makes you want to be free
In a world where we fly, fly, fly.
repeat ad lib. to fade

Could It Be Magic

Hold me, baby;
Feel the magic, feel the magic now.

Verse 1
Spirits move me every time I'm near you,
Whirling like a cyclone in my mind.
You're my lifeline, angel of my lifetime,
Answer to all answers I can find.

Chorus
Baby I want you; come, come,
Come into my arms,
Let me feel the wonder of all of you.
Could it be magic now, now,
Now and hold on fast,
Could this be the magic at last?
Magic...

Verse 2
Baby take me high upon a hillside,
High up where the stallion meets the sun.
I could love you, build my world around you,
Never leave you till my life is done.

Chorus
Baby I want you; come, come,
Come into my arms,
Let me feel the wonder of all of you.
Could it be magic now, now,
Now and hold on fast,
Could this be the magic at last?
Magic...

There is magic in your eyes,
Doo doo wah...

D.S.
Spirits move me every time I'm near you,
Whirling like a cyclone in my mind.

Chorus
Baby I want you; come, come,
Come into my arms,
Let me feel the wonder of all of you.
Could it be magic now, now,
Now and hold on fast,
Could this be the magic at last?
repeat to fade